In the heat of the Scribble

The political cartoons of *Tim*

BOOKMARKS

London, Chicago and Melbourne

In the heat of the Scribble – Tim
First published November 1995
Bookmarks 265 Seven Sisters Road, London N4 2DE, England
Bookmarks, PO Box 16085, Chicago Il. 60616, USA
Bookmarks, GPO Box 1473N, Melbourne 3001, Australia
Copyright c Bookmarks

ISBN 1 898876 12 6

Printed by J Winston and Co Ltd
Cover design by Tim

The Socialist Workers Party is one of an international grouping of socialist organisations:
- **Australia:** International Socialists, PO Box A338, Sydney South, NSW 2000
- **Belgium:** Socialisme International, Rue Lovinfosse 60, 4030 Grivengée, Belgium
- **Britain:** Socialist Workers Party, PO Box 82, London E3
- **Canada:** International Socialists, PO Box 339, Station E, Toronto, Ontario M6H 4E3
- **Cyprus:** Ergatiki Demokratia, PO Box 7280, Nicosia
- **Denmark:** Internationale Socialister, Postboks 642, 2200 København N, Denmark
- **France:** Socialisme International, BP 189, 75926 Paris Cedex 19
- **Greece:** Organosi Sosialisliki Epanastasi, c/o Workers Solidarity, PO Box 8161, Athens 100 10, Greece
- **Holland:** International Socialists, PO Box 9720, 3506 GR Utrecht
- **Ireland:** Socialist Workers Movement, PO Box 1648, Dublin 8
- **New Zealand:** International Socialist Organization, PO Box 6157, Dunedin, New Zealand
- **Norway:** Internasjonale Socialisterr, Postboks 9226 Gronland 0134 Oslo
- **Poland:** Solidarność Socjalistyczna, PO Box 12, 01-900 Warszawa 118
- **South Africa:** International Socialists of South Africa, PO Box 18530, Hillbrow 2038, Johannesberg
- **United States:** International Socialist Organisation, PO Box 16085, Chicago, Illinois 60616
- **Zimbabwe:** International Socialists, PO Box 6758, Harare

Bookmarks is a publishing imprint for Bookmarks Publications Ltd

Contents

Foreword

Too often, we socialist writers are, as they say, at a loss for words. The astonishing horror of the world around us, the determination with which the people in charge gather up their profit with reckless disregard for the consequences often leave us, literally, speechless. Dissatisfied with repeating the same old formulae, nervous of cliches, we often turn aside from the fundamentals into strange by-ways of language which confuse us every bit as much as we confuse our readers. We are constrained too by the desire to appear 'serious'. The very word 'serious' is a sacred one in our movement. 'We must be serious about this' people say. So seriousness in all its turgid forms can come to plague what we write and bore us all silly.

None of these luxuries—flamboyant language, seriousness, using ten words where one will do—are available to political cartoonists. For them, digression is disastrous, seriousness lethal. They have to sum up in a single space (or at best a strip of spaces) an idea which may be impossible to grasp from a thousand words—and to do it in a way that is instantly comprehensible and funny. Insulting the enemy, humiliating him, savaging him—all these are crucial to our struggles. But nothing is more enjoyable than laughing at him. Equally, on the other side, the rulers can often put up with vitriol and abuse. They seldom tolerate mockery.

Words can be effective weapons, but words which mock hurt most. Cartoons, therefore, can strike far deeper than words. I confess that, for years, every time I have picked up the *Socialist Worker* I turn at once to page 2, or wherever Tim's cartoon is published (sometimes, when it is at its very best, it makes the front page). I do so not just for light relief (though that is probably the main reason) but also because Tim very often sums up in his tiny space all the anger and class hatred we feel. He is an expert draughtsman, and cares about his work. His curiously wispy caricatures are unique. His expertise could carry him high into the capitalist press, but it won't—because it is inextricably mingled with his commitment to getting rid of this rotten hierarchical capitalist system and replacing it with a democratic socialist one.

It is high time that these wonderful cartoons were available in a permanent collection. When you've read this book and enjoyed it, buy another one as a present for a friend or relative, preferably one who is not already a socialist and therefore who, when he or she savours Tim's cartoons, will inevitably become one.

Paul Foot

(Where a topical quote, a few facts and figures or some explanation helps illuminate a cartoon we've tried to supply it. Most of the time we've let the images speak for themselves.)

Know your enemies . . .

TARGETTING BENEFITS

"CHARISMATIC" LEADER OF CULT 'HOLD UP" IN
ISOLATED HOUSE -SHOCK

February 1995
Natwest Bank Profits —£1.5 billion
Chief executive's bonus —£100,000
Workers' wage rise —£0.00

'One of the charges at the time of course was that in some way I must have known because I had been the chancellor, the foreign secretary, the prime minister. And therefore I must have known what was going on, but I didn't'. John Major speaking on illegal sales of arms to Iraq during the Gulf War in 1992.

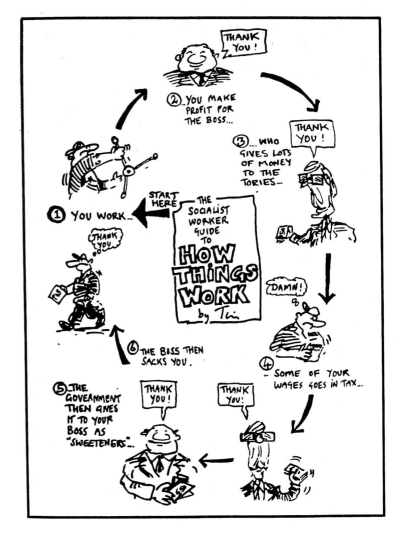

'*A crusade of personal morality*' was how the government described its Back to Basics campaign launched in 1994. In the weeks following a whole series of sex scandals rocked the Tories, probably the most bizzare of which involved Tory MP Stephen Milligan who was found dead with a plastic bag over his head, an orange stuffed in his mouth and wearing nothing but stockings and suspenders.

August 1993, Christchurch. The Tories suffer their biggest by-election defeat since 1945.

. . . and your friends

According to her colleagues Cherry Blair — lawyer and wife to intrepid Labour leader Tony — is 'something of a favourite' with local councils trying to hunt down poll tax non-payers. In 1992 she attempts to send young unemployed man Martin Jaques back to prison for not being able to afford to pay the tax out of his £46 per week dole.

September 1992 and Norman Willis steps down after what seems like an age as 'leader' of the Trades Union Congress.

WE'RE LOOKING FOR SOMEONE WITH THE CHARISMA, ENERGY AND DETERMINATION TO REPLACE NORMAN WILLIS, WE THOUGHT YOU MIGHT BE INTERESTED IN THE JOB...

JUST SOME OF THE LEFT WING FIREBRANDS WAITING TO STEP INTO NORMAN WILLIS'S SHOES.

MODERN TRADE UNIONISM No 63

IN THE INTERESTS OF SPEED AND EFFICIENCY WE'VE DECIDED TO SELL OUT THIS STRIKE...

BEFORE IT HAPPENS!

UNION negotiation EXPLAINED...

Two tier fears

The government's offer of a 1% wage rise in 1995 is met with the biggest display of anger and unity in the health service since 1982, with strike and protest action in over 400 hospitals all over Britain.

'It is right to stop hospitals treating too many people.' Virginia Bottomley, then health secretary, justifying hospital closures in London, 1993.

LONDON'S NEW IMPROVED AMBULANCE SERVICE

September 1995. An 85 % vote for all out indefinite strike action by porters, cleaners, nurses, clerical workers catering and switchboard staff at UCLH in London forced managers to back down and drop charges against union rep Dave Carr. *'Don't let them dare try this again—we'll keep on fighting'*, said one of Dave's supporters.

PRIVATE ENTERPRISE AT SCHOOL

'There is no evidence whatsoever of widespread student hardship'. Tim Boswell, Education minister.

Private hell

On the gravy train—
BR boss Robert Reid,
£344,000 for a 3 day week.
Railtrack chairman Bob
Horton, £121,000 for a 3 day
week.
Chief exec. John Edmonds,
£132,000 basic.
Finance director Norman
Broadhurst, £150,000 basic.
Director of safety David
Rayner, £90,000 basic.

Cruel world

General election 1992.
'The very process of selling themselves as models of moderation has deprived Mr Smith and his Labour colleagues of anything distinctive.'
Ian Aitkin, The Guardian.

A DANGEROUS OUTBREAK OF ELECTION FEVER AT No 17 RIDGWAY HOUSE EAST BRINKLY

The Child Support Agency included a 14 year old girl's 94p a week interest from a National Savings account in its assesment of her divorced father's income. Tory minister Alistair Burt admitted it was government policy to count children's pocket money in maintenance assessments.

Early 1995. British gas boss Cedric Brown awards himself a 75% wage rise, a £593,000 bonus and £268,000 share handout. Gas bills go up by nearly 3%.

Unite and fight

'How do you intellectualise when you punch the hell out of a nigger? You keep choking him out until he tells you the truth. A lot of policemen will get a kick out of it.'
'First thing out of a nigger's mouth for the first five or six sentences is a fucking lie.'
Los Angeles policeman Mark Fuhrman, key prosecution witness in OJ Simpson trial.

In 1992 four LA policemen hit Rodney King, a local black man, a total of 56 times in what they described as a 'group beat'. *I'm a victim and Rodney King is a criminal'*, said Sgt Koon, one of the policemen involved.

June 1993 and 150 internees at the Campsfield refugee centre stage a hunger strike against conditions there. The private police force, Group 4, initiate a reign of terror to force inmates to sign deportation papers.

The East End is being invaded by frightening strangers with an alien culture, who talk strangely, and dress strangely AND DON'T belong here...

By 1995 the fascist British National Party's electoral strategy of standing candidates in local elections is in tatters thanks to the efforts of anti racists and the Anti Nazi League. But their threat in the future cannot be ignored.

Vultures

Vultures cackled over our corpses:
their old dreams had taken shape:
we were carrion at last

Vultures scoured and cleaned
tidied up the carnage,
wanting no left overs.

Vultures are looming now —
they hover over high-rise wrecks
and hungry queues,
hunting bodies,
screeching 'Corpses? What Corpses?
We're pretty boys!'

Parading as parrots
they don't fool us
because we are the leftovers,
the ones that poison vultures.   *Michael Rosen*

Bang to rights

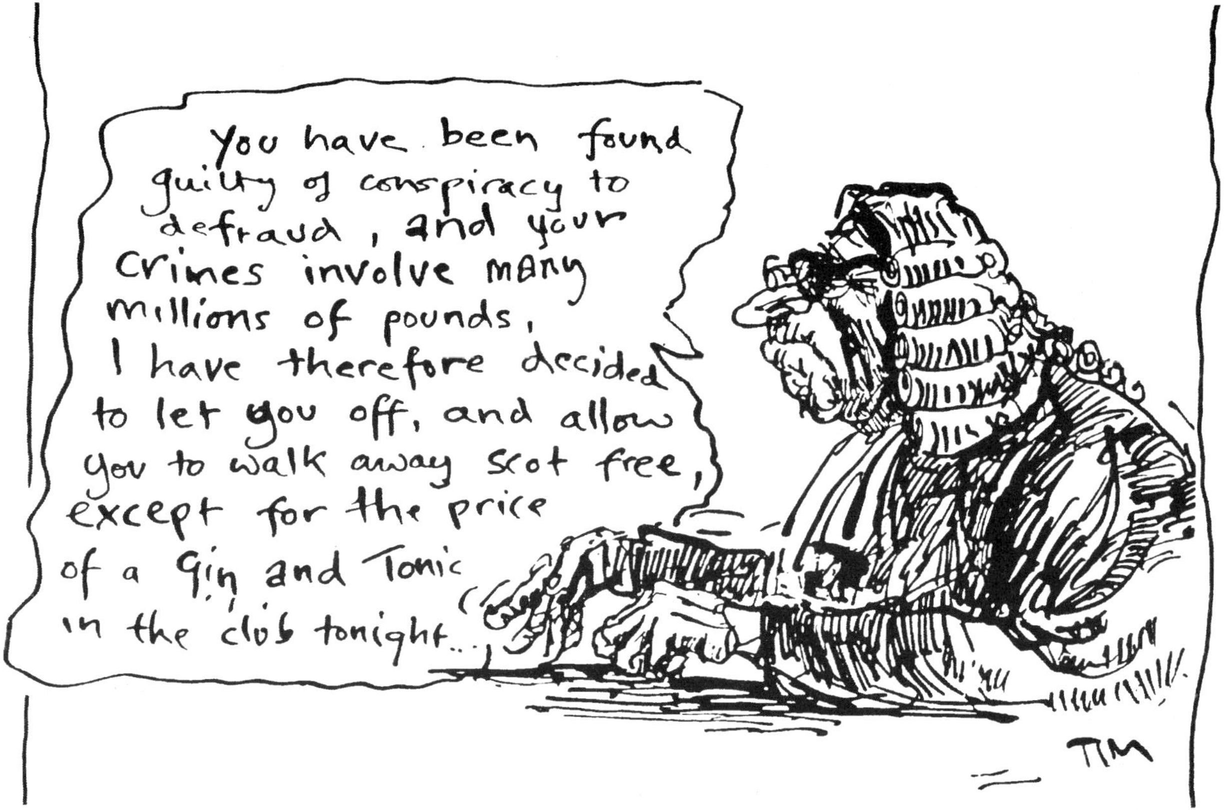

September 1995.
BT bosses allow
police to use BT
vans and equipment
while on
surveillance.

Apocalypse now

DEEP CONCERN OVER THE PLIGHT OF THE SOMALIANS

'I thought it would be great to get some insight into my heritage, but I feel really different, way different. They look at me like I'm on the other side'.
US Marine in Somalia after the US invade in 1992.

SOMALI WAR LORD

INTERNATIONAL
PEACEKEEPER

BLOODY DEFENCE CUTS!

In 1985 Live Aid raised £50 million for the starving of Ethiopia. That year the country had to pay £65 million in interest payments on loans from Western banks. At the same time 40 million tons of grain — enough to feed the starving ten times over — were stockpiled in Europe at a cost of £5 billion a year.

Banana monarchy

1982. The Queen Mother is rushed to hospital when a fish bone gets lodged in her throat.

1992. £100m of tax payers money goes on repairing Windsor Castle after a fire there. The Queen's personal wealth is estimated at £6,500m, of which £19m comes from share dividends, or about £52,000 per day.

FOLLOWING THE PRESS COUNCIL'S RULING, SOCIALIST WORKER OFFERS A FURTHER SUGGESTION ON HOW NEWSPAPERS SHOULD COVER THE ROYALS

Merry xmas

RUDOLPH THE BROWN NOSED REINDEER.

WELL TO BE HONEST GABRIEL, IT SEEMS LIKE A LOT OF TROUBLE TO GO TO JUST TO GET A COUNCIL FLAT..

Q. Why is Santa always so happy?

HO, HO, HO!

A. Because he doesn't have to spend Christmas with his family

CAPTAIN OATS LEAVES TO CLAIM HIS COLD WEATHER ALLOWANCE.

Some advice . . .

"MAKE THE BULLETIN READABLE..."